Language Readers

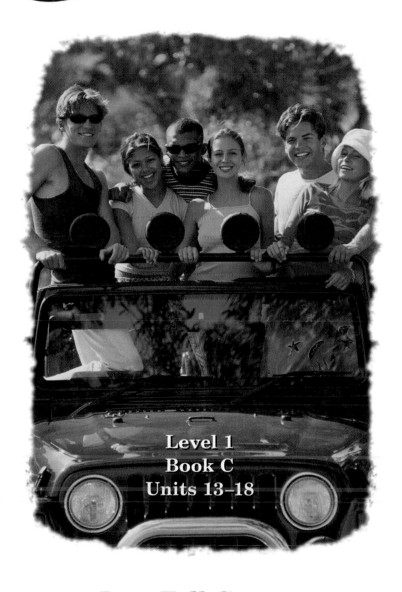

Level 1
Book C
Units 13–18

Jane Fell Greene
Judy Fell Woods

Text layout and design by Kimberly Harris
Cover design by Becky Malone
Cover Image © 2000 by Digital Vision Ltd.
Illustrated by Peggy Ranson

This product is in compliance with AB2519 California State
Adoption revision requirements.

Printed in the United States of America

Published and Distributed by

SOPRIS
WEST

4093 Specialty Place   •   Longmont, CO 80504   •   (303) 651-2829
www.sopriswest.com

Contents

Unit 13, Book 1 The Class Trip 1

Unit 13, Book 2 A Thrill at the Track 11

Unit 13, Book 3 The Twins' Swim Trip 21

Unit 14, Book 1 Mr. and Mrs. Grunch 31

Unit 14, Book 2 Bud and Nick Huff and Puff . . . 41

Unit 14, Book 3 Much Fuss on a Bus 51

Unit 15, Book 1 The Velvet Jacket. 61

Unit 15, Book 2 Talcum and Twins 71

Unit 15, Book 3 At the Campus 81

Unit 16, Book 1 The Spring Picnic 91

Unit 16, Book 2 Scram! 101

Unit 16, Book 3 A Big Splash 111

Unit 17, Book 1 Pumpkins, Masks, and Goblins . 123

Unit 17, Book 2 At Camp 135

Unit 17, Book 3 The Landfill. 147

Unit 18, Book 1 A Match for Chick 157

Unit 18, Book 2 The Hatchback 167

Unit 18, Book 3 Fantastic Bash at Sunset 179

Unit 13, Book 1

THE CLASS TRIP

UNIT 13

Phonology/Orthography Concepts

- **Initial blends** are consonant letters representing two different consonant phonemes (sounds) at the beginning of a word.

- Unit 13 initial blends are: **bl**, **gl**, **cl**, **pl**, **fl**, **sl**, **br**, **fr**, **tr**, **cr**, **dr**, **gr**, **pr**, **shr**, **thr**, **sc**, **sm**, **sn**, **sp**, **sk**, **st**, **sw**, **tw**, and **dw**.

Vocabulary

black	crash	fresh	snack	thrill
blocks	crab	glad	snap	trash
Brad	cross	grill	spot	trick
brag	drag	plan	stack	trip
brick	drinks	plot	stand	twin
brim	drop	shrank	stick	
brisk	flag	shrill	sticks	
clam	flap	skill	stiff	*they*
clap	flash	slim	still	*your*
class	flat	smash	stink	
clock	flock	smell	swim	

2

THE CLASS
TRIP

Story Summary:

Miss Pitt's class is planning a class trip. The students each have different ideas about where the class should go. After each possible trip is discussed, the children vote by standing when the trip they like best is announced by Miss Pitt.

Miss Pitt's class has a wish. They think of plans to have a class trip.

Sid and Nick plot to stop back at the long ship at the dock. They could tell the class of fish, clams, shells, and nets. They could brag of long flat bass and fresh cod fish.

Tam and Pat plan a trip to Big Ben, a big tin clock with a black bell that rings and a flat red flag that flaps on top.

They would have to cross six blocks to get to the clock, Big Ben, yet they would have a thrill when they got to it.

Al plans a swim trip. Al would wish that the class could get to a hot spot, swim, and snack.

With sticks, they could get shells and clams. They could fish off the dock for black bass and fresh cod.

Mat thinks, "I can plan the snacks. Hot dogs and chips with pop to drink would have the class well fed."

 "I will have to get a grill and trash bags. The trash will stink if it is not in trash bags."

Sam has plans to have a bus trip. The class could get on the red and black bus with the flat grill. They could bring pals.

Miss Pitt said, "Which trip will win? If it is the trip you want, stand."

Sam got up for the bus trip. When Miss Pitt said, "Big Ben," six kids got up. Al and Pat got up when Miss Pitt said, "swim trip."

A flock of kids got up as Miss Pitt said, "a trip to a long ship." The long ship trip wins. Sid and Nick clap and sing, "It is a thrill to win!"

Teacher/Parent Pages

Use the following questions to stimulate language growth, imagination, conceptual relationships, and higher-level thinking skills. These activities will encourage conversation and help develop language skills. Students must know that their ideas are important and that their questions will be heard. Have fun and accept all reasonable answers while praising and encouraging questioning from the students.

Vocabulary Expansion

Describe and define these words and phrases:

plan	imagine	decide
class trip	destination	discuss
wish list	grill (car)	tally
ideas	grill (charcoal)	
flock	clock tower	
vote	thrill	

Language Expansion Activities

1. Draw a picture of a place where you would like to go with your class. Write about it.

2. Ask your teacher to let your class vote on something (a book to read, a trip to take, a picture, etc.). Let each person stand up to vote, and tally the results on the board. Predict what will happen.

Language Expansion Questions

1. What were the children in Miss Pitt's class planning?

2. Where did Sid and Nick want to go?

3. What was Mat planning?

4. How did the children vote? Which trip won the vote?

5. How do you think the class will get to the ship?

6. Imagine where you would want to go if your class was planning a trip.

7. Mat was planning the menu for the trip. What would you bring along to eat on your trip? Make a list of the foods you would take.

8. In what ways will the class trip be like the scout trip in the Unit 12 story, *Ken Bell*?

9. If you could have voted in this story, which trip would you have voted for?

10. Change the story so that another trip wins. How would the story be different? Write a new ending.

Unit 13, Book 2

A THRILL AT THE TRACK

UNIT 13

Phonology/Orthography Concepts

- **Initial blends** are consonant letters representing two different consonant phonemes (sounds) at the beginning of a word.

- Unit 13 initial blends are: **bl**, **gl**, **cl**, **pl**, **fl**, **sl**, **br**, **fr**, **tr**, **cr**, **dr**, **gr**, **pr**, **shr**, **thr**, **sc**, **sm**, **sn**, **sp**, **sk**, **st**, **sw**, **tw**, and **dw**.

Vocabulary

black	crash	fresh	snack	thrill
blocks	crab	glad	snap	trash
Brad	cross	grill	spot	trick
brag	drag	plan	stack	trip
brick	drinks	plot	stand	twin
brim	drop	shrank	stick	
brisk	flag	shrill	sticks	
clam	flap	skill	stiff	*they*
clap	flash	slim	still	*your*
class	flat	smash	stink	
clock	flock	smell	swim	

12

A THRILL AT
THE TRACK

Story Summary:

Ken Bell's scouts are on an outing at the Zig Zag Race Track. The boys are thrilled just to be there, but when Ken introduces them to a driver, Brad Brick, they become even more enthusiastic. Brad and his men are in the pit fixing his race car, #10, which was in a crash last week at Drag Track. The scouts finally get seated and begin to watch the race. Brad's hot rod leads the pack until there is a crash at Zig Zag Pass. Brad comes out ahead of the pack and wins the race.

Ken Bell and his pack are at Zig Zag Track.

Men and gals have hot rods at the track. The big thrill is to pass the flag and win with your hot rod.

The trick at the track is this: to get to the red and black flag in a flash and win.

The track has a long quick path and a zig zag spot. This spot can shock and trip men and let them crash and smash the hot rods.

Ken is pals with the man in the stiff pink cap, Brad Brick. Brad has a #10 on his cap.

Brad's hot rod, #10, had a crash at Drag Track. The grill on #10 got hot and shrank as it fell on to the stiff wall.

Brad and his men have to fix the grill quick. They are in the pit.

Ken yells, "Brad, will your hot rod win at this track?"

"You can bet on it!" yells Brad Brick. The kids get a thrill when Brad yells to them!

Brad gets in #10. The flag drops and the hot rods are off. Brad has to cross Zig Zag Track's path in a flash to win. Nick yells, "Press the pack, Brad. Win it!"

Smash! Crash! Wham! The shrill crash is at Zig Zag Pass. Six hot rods  smash. Brad has a quick pit stop. His grill is hot. His men fix it with skill and Brad is still at the top of the pack.

The red and black flag drops as Brad zips in to win! The pack has a big thrill. "You did it, Brad!" the pals yell.

Teacher/Parent Pages

Use the following questions to stimulate language growth, imagination, conceptual relationships, and higher-level thinking skills. These activities will encourage conversation and help develop language skills. Students must know that their ideas are important and that their questions will be heard. Have fun and accept all reasonable answers while praising and encouraging questioning from the students.

Vocabulary Expansion

Describe and define these words and phrases:

racetrack	checkered flag	pit stop
skill	introduce	pack
zig zag path	equipment	ahead
hot rod	enthusiastic	crash
driver	pit	fans

Language Expansion Activities

1. Use paint or clay to fashion a racetrack with a pit stop, race cars, and bleachers for the fans. Pretend you are a driver. Tell about your race.

2. Practice introducing your friends to teachers, parents, and other people.

Language Expansion Questions

1. Where did Ken Bell take the boys?

2. What do race car drivers have to do at the track?

3. What was the name of the driver who was Ken's friend? What number was on his pink hot rod?

4. There was a crash at Zig Zag Pass. Imagine what happened and tell about it.

5. Why did Brad have to take his car in for a pit stop?

6. If you could interview a race car driver, what kinds of questions would you ask? List the questions and act out the interview with one of your friends.

7. Which part of the story did you like the best? Why?

8. Many brave men and women drive race cars. Suppose that you are a race car driver. Write a story about some events that might happen to you.

9. "A race car driver has a more exciting life than I do." Decide whether the statement is true or false. Explain.

10. Race tracks are exciting. What are some other exciting places where kids can go with their parents, teachers, or scout leaders? Write or tell about them.

THE TWINS' SWIM TRIP

UNIT 13

Phonology/Orthography Concepts

- **Initial blends** are consonant letters representing two different consonant phonemes (sounds) at the beginning of a word.

- Unit 13 initial blends are: **bl**, **gl**, **cl**, **pl**, **fl**, **sl**, **br**, **fr**, **tr**, **cr**, **dr**, **gr**, **pr**, **shr**, **thr**, **sc**, **sm**, **sn**, **sp**, **sk**, **st**, **sw**, **tw**, and **dw**.

Vocabulary

black	crash	fresh	snack	thrill
blocks	crab	glad	snap	trash
Brad	cross	grill	spot	trick
brag	drag	plan	stack	trip
brick	drinks	plot	stand	twin
brim	drop	shrank	stick	
brisk	flag	shrill	sticks	
clam	flap	skill	stiff	*they*
clap	flash	slim	still	*your*
class	flat	smash	stink	
clock	flock	smell	swim	

22

THE TWINS' SWIM TRIP

Story Summary:

It's Dad's day off and he takes the kids to the beach for the day. Tam and Sis pack the cooler, get the picnic basket, and fix the food for the outing. It is the twins' first time at the beach and they decide to pack their favorite things, too. They arrive at the beach and Dad gives Tam a lesson in crabbing. Sis and the twins swim and fix the food. Tam catches her first crab and the whole family has a great time.

Dad was not at his job. Dad and Tam had the twins, Bill and Jill, and Sis. "It's hot," said Dad. "Let's have a swim trip!"

The kids are glad. "Yes," said Tam. "We can net crabs."

Sis packs the black swim bag as Tam gets the snacks.

"Let's bring chips and frost pops," yells Sis.

"We can have them," said Tam. "We will have hot dogs on sticks as well."

As Dad packs the van, the kids get the fresh snacks. Bill drops his jack-in-the-box as Jill drags the bag of blocks. Tam and Sis bring the flat tin box with the snacks.

"Is the pink pop in that box?" said Dad.

"Yes, Dad, it is in the box."

The kids pack in to the van and Dad gets to the spot in a flash.

As they cross the wet path, Sis yells, "Dad! That stack of clams is as big as a ship!"

"Well," Dad tells Sis, "it's not that big."

"I can smell fresh crabs," Tam tells Dad.

As they put the bags on the swim pad, Dad tells Tam, "Tam, to get a crab, put a bit of fish on a string, snap the string in, then net the crabs when they nip on the fish."

"Is this your string, Dad?" said Tam.

"Yes, get it. I will grab the fish, nets, and crab pot."

Bill and Jill step, hop, skip, and get wet. "Scat," yells Bill to a crab. Sis swims with the twins as Dad and Tam get crabs.

"Dad! Dad!" yells Tam, "A crab bit the fish. I have it on the string!"

"Get it in the net, Tam," yells Dad. "Grab it quick!"

"I got it," said Tam as Dad put the crab in the pot.

Sis and the twins get the snacks. Dad tells Sis to get the pop. "Fill it to the brim," said Dad. They could not miss.

"Thanks, Dad," the kids said.

Teacher/Parent Pages

Use the following questions to stimulate language growth, imagination, conceptual relationships, and higher-level thinking skills. These activities will encourage conversation and help develop language skills. Students must know that their ideas are important and that their questions will be heard. Have fun and accept all reasonable answers while praising and encouraging questioning from the students.

Vocabulary Expansion

Describe and define these words and phrases:

day off	outing	lesson
beach	arrive	family
cooler	decide	swim bag
pack	crabbing	frost pop
picnic basket	clams	to the brim

Language Expansion Activities

1. Act out some of the things you can do at the beach. See if your pals can identify your pantomimes.

2. Ask your teacher or parents to take you to a lake or beach or pool on a field trip. When you get back, write about your adventures. If you do not have a water area near you, read a good book about a beach trip.

Language Expansion Questions

1. Which of Tam's parents had a day off?

2. Where did he decide to take the family?

3. What things did the twins pack? What things did Sis and Tam pack? Try to remember all of the things Dad packed into the van.

4. What did Dad teach Tam to do at the beach?

5. Do you think the children enjoyed their day at the beach? Why?

6. Make a list of things you would pack if you were going to the beach. Don't forget the sunscreen!

7. The twins seemed to enjoy their first day at the beach. Do you remember the first time you ever went to the beach? Write a story about it.

8. Dad taught Tam how to go crabbing. Can you think of anything a grown-up ever taught you? Describe the lessons.

9. At the end of the story, the children thanked their dad for taking them on the outing to the beach. When was the last time you thanked someone for doing something for you? If you can't remember, thank someone the next time someone does something nice for you.

10. Dad took the children to the beach. Name some other places families can go together to have fun.

MR. AND MRS. GRUNCH

UNIT 14

Phonology/Orthography Concepts

- A single unit of sound is a phoneme.
  - Vowel phonemes are open sounds.
  - Consonant phonemes are closed sounds.
  - Combined phonemes create words we hear.
- Letters are symbols that represent phonemes.
  - Combined letters create words we write and read.
  - Vowel sound-symbol relationship: short /u/

Vocabulary

blush	flung	jump	tub	*Mr.*
Bud	fuss	just	rush	*Mrs.*
bugs	grump	luck	shrubs	*Ms.*
bunks	Grunch	lunch	stuck	
bus	gum	much	stuff	
but	help	mud	stung	
Chung	hub	munch	such	
chunk	huff	nuts	up	
crush	hug	puff	us	
cups	hunch	rub		
cut	hush	too		

MR. AND MRS. GRUNCH

Story Summary:

Nick and his younger brother, Bud, are invited to have lunch at Tam's house. When they discover that they have missed the bus, they cut through the property of Mr. and Mrs. Grunch, two grouchy people who don't like kids. In his hurry, Bud drops his toy truck. He goes back after it. Bud is nearly captured by Mr. Grunch, but is saved by his older brother, Nick.

Bud, a kid that was just six, went with Nick to Tam's to grill hot dogs. Nick had said they would hop on the bus, but the bus sped off.

Nick said, "Let's cut in to the shrubs in back of Mr. and Mrs. Grunch's. We have to rush!"

"They are cross," said Bud. "They will snap and yell at us to get off the grass. They could grab us!"

Nick said to Bud, "They can not grab us. I can run fast! Let's run, Bud. Mr. Grunch will not get us!"

Mr. Grunch was in the back. "I will trim the stems on this shrub," thinks Mr. Grunch.

Then, when Nick and Bud cut in to his grass and shrubs, he flung a stick at them.

Mrs. Grunch was a prim grump in a dull black dress. "Get off the grass, you brats! You can not cut in and crush the stems and shrubs," Mrs. Grunch said.

———

Nick and Bud fled in a flash. But Bud had left his red truck in Mr. and Mrs. Grunch's grass. Bud ran back in to get his truck. Crash! Bud fell on Mr. and Mrs. Grunch's trash can.

Nick got Bud just when Mr. and Mrs. Grunch had run to grab him.

"Such luck! I was stuck!" said Bud. They ran fast.

"Did I crush the trash can lid?" said Bud. "I fell in the mud, slid, and hit the trash can. This leg is cut bad." Bud's cut bled and bled.

"I can fix your leg, Bud," said Nick, "but you did skin it bad!"

"Thanks, Nick," Bud said. "This trip is just too much!"

Nick had a hug for Bud, but then he said, "You should not have run back for your truck, Bud. You did not have to bring it to Tam and Sis's."

"But Nick," Bud said, "in class, Sis said that I should bring the red truck when you and I went to lunch!" Nick and Bud had to rush to get to Tam and Sis's.

Teacher/Parent Pages

Use the following questions to stimulate language growth, imagination, conceptual relationships, and higher-level thinking skills. These activities will encourage conversation and help develop language skills. Students must know that their ideas are important and that their questions will be heard. Have fun and accept all reasonable answers while praising and encouraging questioning from the students.

Vocabulary Expansion

Describe and define these words and phrases:

cut in	discover	private
fled	miss the bus	scold
in a flash	grouchy	rush
property	in a hurry	on time
invited	capture	saved

Language Expansion Activities

1. Make a map that shows these places: Bud and Nick's house; Tam and Sis's house; the bus route; Mr. and Mrs. Grunch's house; the dock. Print the names of all the places.

2. Explain why Mr. and Mrs. Grunch might feel the way they do about kids. Then write a story that tells what events might have made Mr. and Mrs. Grunch feel the way they do.

Language Expansion Questions

1. Where were Nick and Bud invited?

2. Why did the brothers cut through the Grunches' private property?

3. What did Mr. and Mrs. Grunch do when they discovered Nick and Bud on their property?

4. Why did Nick have to run back to get Bud? What had Bud dropped?

5. Why do you think Nick and Bud were in such a hurry?

6. When people are invited to someone else's home, why is it important to be on time?

7. How do you think Nick felt about his younger brother? Explain why you think so.

8. What is meant by private property? What private property do you own? How would you feel about someone using it without your permission?

9. What do you suppose Mr. Grunch might have done if he had caught Bud? What would he have told Bud? Have you ever been scolded? Why?

10. In the story, Nick and Bud made a poor decision. Try to remember a time you made a poor decision. What other choices did you have? What should you have done? Write about it.

BUD AND NICK HUFF AND PUFF

UNIT 14

Phonology/Orthography Concepts

- A single unit of sound is a phoneme.
  - Vowel phonemes are open sounds.
  - Consonant phonemes are closed sounds.
  - Combined phonemes create words we hear.
- Letters are symbols that represent phonemes.
  - Combined letters create words we write and read.
  - Vowel sound-symbol relationship: short /u/

Vocabulary

blush	flung	jump	tub	*Mr.*
Bud	fuss	just	rush	*Mrs.*
bugs	grump	luck	shrubs	*Ms.*
bunks	Grunch	lunch	stuck	
bus	gum	much	stuff	
but	help	mud	stung	
Chung	hub	munch	such	
chunk	huff	nuts	up	
crush	hug	puff	us	
cups	hunch	rub		
cut	hush	too		

BUD AND NICK
HUFF AND PUFF

Story Summary:

Nick and his younger brother, Bud, are late for lunch at Tam and Sis's house. They have to run twelve blocks to get there, and they become exhausted. Nick, who has a crush on Tam, thinks it is worth it; Bud is not so certain. They grill hot dogs and have a delightful time eating outdoors.

Nick and Bud had run six blocks, but they still had six blocks to get to Tam and Sis's. They had to huff and puff.

At last, Nick and Bud got to Tam's block. They could smell the hot dogs on the grill. Nick got his brush. He had a big grin. Nick had a crush on Tam.

Sis said, "Tam, this is Bud. He is in Mrs. Smith's class with us. You can help, Bud. Let's get the pink pop. Tam and I had to chill it."

"Tam, you are a slick gal," Nick said. "You should not blush, Tam. And you did not have to have such a big fuss. This is just swell!"

Sis and Bud got on the swings. Bud smacks his lips and drinks his pop. "This is lots of fun!" Bud said to Sis. "Did you get chips to munch on?"

Tam said to Sis, "Red bugs have stung the twins. Mom said to rub this stuff on them. Then they have to have a nap. Can you help, Sis?"

"Bud and I can cut the hot dog buns," Nick said. "Just stack the cups and things at the grill and I will get lunch on."

Sis and Tam went in with the twins. Bud said to Nick, "This was such a long trip! And I got in to a mess. I had to huff and puff to get to Sis's. Will you tell Mom and Dad what I did?"

"I will not tell," Nick said. "You and I can catch the bus to get back. It stops at this block. We will get back quick."

As Nick cut the buns, Bud got the chips and nuts and pop. They put the lunch things on. "It is not too bad to have to huff and puff," said Bud, "when you have this much fun!"

When Tam and Sis got back, the kids sat and had lunch. Nick, Sis, Tam, and Bud had lots of fun.

Teacher/Parent Pages

Use the following questions to stimulate language growth, imagination, conceptual relationships, and higher-level thinking skills. These activities will encourage conversation and help develop language skills. Students must know that their ideas are important and that their questions will be heard. Have fun and accept all reasonable answers while praising and encouraging questioning from the students.

Vocabulary Expansion

Describe and define these words and phrases:

huff and puff	have a crush on	chill the pop
exhausted	make a fuss	smacks his lips
worth it	get lunch on	blush
run twelve blocks	grill	catch the bus
certain	delightful	a quick trip

Language Expansion Activities

1. Draw a picture of a time you ate outdoors. Then, write a story to tell about it.

2. Tam and Sis help their mom with the twins, who are very small. Make a chart and list all of the things that must be done for very small children.

Language Expansion Questions

1. Why did Nick get out his brush when he got near Tam's house?

2. Can you think of any reasons why Tam made a fuss about Nick and Bud coming for lunch?

3. What happened to the twins? What are the best things to do if you are bitten by insects?

4. Bud and Nick helped get lunch ready. What kinds of things can a considerate guest do to help the hosts?

5. Explain why Bud was so concerned that he asked Nick if he was going to tell their mom and dad. Sometimes, it might be best to tell your mom and dad about things that happen. What has happened to you that your mom and dad should have known about?

6. Why do kids sometimes hesitate to tell their parents things, even though they know they should?

7. Tam and Sis have to help their mother with the twins. Discuss the kinds of things that older brothers and sisters can do to help with their younger brothers and sisters.

8. When people have a cookout or a picnic, there are special foods that they enjoy. What special foods do you enjoy when you eat outdoors? What kinds of food are not good for eating outdoors?

9. There is a special season of the year when we particularly enjoy eating outdoors. What season is it? What are the other three seasons? How are they different?

10. Discuss important things to do—and not to do—when you are a guest at someone's home.

MUCH FUSS ON A BUS

UNIT 14

Phonology/Orthography Concepts

- A single unit of sound is a phoneme.
  - Vowel phonemes are open sounds.
  - Consonant phonemes are closed sounds.
  - Combined phonemes create words we hear.
- Letters are symbols that represent phonemes.
  - Combined letters create words we write and read.
  - Vowel sound-symbol relationship: short /u/

Vocabulary

blush	flung	jump	tub	*Mr.*
Bud	fuss	just	rush	*Mrs.*
bugs	grump	luck	shrubs	*Ms.*
bunks	Grunch	lunch	stuck	
bus	gum	much	stuff	
but	help	mud	stung	
Chung	hub	munch	such	
chunk	huff	nuts	up	
crush	hug	puff	us	
cups	hunch	rub		
cut	hush	too		

MUCH FUSS ON A BUS

Story Summary:

Nick and Bud are waiting for a bus. Bud has never ridden a bus before, so Nick gives him advice. Once they are on the bus, trouble starts. Some older kids start throwing rocks. The bus driver throws the older kids off the bus. Bud begins to understand why he should always listen to his parents. Nick gets Bud home and takes care of him.

Nick and Bud went up the block to the bus stop. "The trick is to catch the bus just when it stops," Nick said. "When the bus gets to the stop, do not stand still, Bud. You must get on fast."

Nick sat at the stand. Nick thinks, "A tram just clicks on its tracks, but a bus can rush in a flash. A trip on a bus is brisk. I think it's a thrill to catch a bus."

Bud got a hub cap that fell from a truck. Bud said to Nick, "You and I could catch frogs." Bud put a frog in his hand.

"You can not stop to catch frogs, Bud. Put the frog back in the grass. Drop him! You can not bring frogs on the bus."

Bud put the frog back. "Hush, Bud," Nick said. "Just sit still."

When the bus got to Tam's block, the man put up the bus's red flag and they got on as fast as they could.

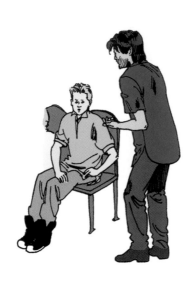

On the bus, a bum went up to Nick and said, "Have you got a stick of gum?" Nick said they did not. The sun got hot as they sat on the bus.

Crash! In a flash, the bus just stops. The man yells,

"What is the big fuss on this bus? Sit still or get off!"

Six big kids from Mrs. Chung's class had chunks of rocks on the bus. They had flung them at the bus's clock. The man was mad!

"Get off!" the man yells at the six kids. "I will get the cops. You kids should not toss rock chunks on a bus."

"This bus has had much fuss," Bud said to Nick. "Mom said I should not get on a bus. If I did what Mom said, I would not get in such a big mess."

"Bud, when we get back, I will put your black sub in the bath tub and you can have a bath. Then I will fix the cut on your leg, and you can put on fresh pants and a top."

"Then, when Mom and Dad get back," Nick went on, "you could tell them of the fuss on the bus."

"Nick," Bud said, "I think I should not tell. The fuss on that bus was just too much!"

Teacher/Parent Pages

Use the following questions to stimulate language growth, imagination, conceptual relationships, and higher-level thinking skills. These activities will encourage conversation and help develop language skills. Students must know that their ideas are important and that their questions will be heard. Have fun and accept all reasonable answers while praising and encouraging questioning from the students.

Vocabulary Expansion

Describe and define these words and phrases:

experienced	hubcap	realize
advice	amuse yourself	bum
a thrill	get kicked off	in a flash
bus stand	recognize	cops
tram	trouble	take care of

Language Expansion Activities

1. Make a list of rules for behavior while riding a bus. Print your list and hang it up in the classroom. Go to other classrooms and read your list to the other students in the school.

2. Bud likes frogs. Select an animal you like and gather information about it. Share the information with others.

Language Expansion Questions

1. What advice did Nick give Bud as they were waiting for the bus?

2. How did Bud amuse himself while they waited?

3. A stranger spoke to Nick on the bus, and asked him for some gum. What should you do if a stranger tries to talk to you? On the bus, who could help you?

4. When Nick saw the bad kids, he recognized them. When you recognize people who are always in trouble, what should you do? Why?

5. Explain why the bus driver lost his temper. What would you have done if you were the bus driver? Do grown-ups ever make mistakes?

6. In the end, Bud was a little afraid. Explain why he felt this way.

7. Bud was not permitted to go on a bus. How do you think Nick might have felt if something bad had happened to his little brother?

8. In the story, the bus driver put up the bus's red flag. Reread that page and figure out what the red flag meant.

9. What kinds of transportation are available in your community? What kinds of transportation have you ridden?

10. Take turns discussing the vehicles you have ridden. Try to determine the best and the worst qualities of each vehicle.

THE VELVET JACKET

UNIT 15

Phonology/Syllabication Concepts

- Phoneme—syllable—word relationships:
  - A word must have at least one vowel phoneme.
  - A word has one or more **syllables**.
  - Each **syllable** contains **one vowel phoneme**.
  - A syllable that ends with a consonant phoneme is a **closed syllable**.

Vocabulary

admit	goblin	rabbit	*into*
basket	insect	ragbag	
Batman	jacket	shamrock	
cactus	locket	splendid	
campus	muffin	sunset	
cannot	napkin	talcum	
catnap	padlock	tickets	
comic	picnic	traffic	
fabric	pigpen	upset	
fantastic	plastic	velvet	
frogman	pockets		

THE VELVET JACKET

Story Summary:

Tam's older cousin, Stan, asks her to go with him to his college campus to see a special show. She is young and her parents aren't sure whether it would be a good idea. They finally decide that she can go as long as her dad drives them to the campus. Tam tells Stan and learns that she must dress up for the show. Her mother helps her pick out a dress to wear and makes her a special jacket. Tam is excited.

Tam felt glad. Her chum and kin, Stan, would ask Tam's mom and dad to bring Tam to his campus. They would chat with the campus comic, Frogman Fred, and they would sing and jam with the kids on the campus.

"Mom and Dad," Tam said, "can Stan bring me to his campus?"

"I think Mom and I would let you," said Dad, "if I could get you there in the van and then pick you and Stan up at sunset."

Ring! Ring! It was Stan. Tam said to him, "Mom and Dad said yes, but Dad must bring us in his van and pick us up at sunset."

"Must I dress up?" said Tam.

"Yes, the kids on campus will dress up," Stan said to Tam. "You can put on a fantastic dress, Tam. You will have fun."

"What a thrill," said Tam to Mom. "But I must dress up."

"Yes," said Mom. "What will you put on?"

"I am a bit upset. I do not have a splendid dress," said Tam, "but I could put on the red dress with the black zigzag cuffs."

"Yes," said Mom. "And I have some black velvet fabric. I will cut it and fix you a black velvet jacket with pockets. A jacket would jazz up your red dress."

"Thanks, Mom. I will get the fabric." Mom cut the fabric and in a flash Tam had a splendid black velvet jacket.

"You can have the slim black bag in the plastic box on the bed," Mom said to Tam.

"Mom, thanks! I cannot miss with the jacket and the black bag!"

As Mom went to press the hems on the jacket, Tam said, "Mom, can I have a snack?"

"You can have a hot bran muffin on a napkin, Tam. They are in the picnic basket," Mom said.

"Thanks," said Tam. "I have a fantastic mom. You are tops!"

Teacher/Parent Pages

Use the following questions to stimulate language growth, imagination, conceptual relationships, and higher-level thinking skills. These activities will encourage conversation and help develop language skills. Students must know that their ideas are important and that their questions will be heard. Have fun and accept all reasonable answers while praising and encouraging questioning from the students.

Vocabulary Expansion

Describe and define these words and phrases:

university	idea	jazz up
campus	chaperone	traffic
comedian	event	kin
restriction	dress up	fabric
discuss	excited	dull

Language Expansion Activities

1. Get some scrap fabric from your teacher or from home and cut out a piece of clothing for a doll or a stick puppet. Glue or sew the pieces together and dress up the doll. Describe to your pals how you did this. List the steps.

2. Write a story about kids playing dress up at school or at home.

Language Expansion Questions

1. Who was Tam's kin and chum? Do you have a favorite cousin?

2. Where did Stan want Tam to go? Why?

3. What did Tam's parents say about Tam going with Stan?

4. When Tam learned that she had to dress up, she was upset because she didn't have a new dress. What did her mom do to help her?

5. What else did Tam's mom let her have for the event?

6. Tam's parents let her go to the campus with her cousin only if her dad could chaperone the event. Do your parents ever let you do something, but with restrictions?

7. Use information from the story to list the things you know about Tam's mom.

8. Describe your mom or dad. What important things can parents do for kids? Write about them.

9. Suppose Tam's mom had not had any black fabric. What are some other ways she might have helped Tam dress up?

10. Tam was upset because she didn't have a pretty dress to wear. Have you ever been upset because you didn't have something you really needed or wanted? Write or tell about it.

TALCUM AND TWINS

UNIT 15

Phonology/Syllabication Concepts

- Phoneme—syllable—word relationships:
  - A word must have at least one vowel phoneme.
  - A word has one or more **syllables**.
  - Each **syllable** contains **one vowel phoneme**.
  - A syllable that ends with a consonant phoneme is a **closed syllable**.

Vocabulary

admit	goblin	rabbit	*into*
basket	insect	ragbag	
Batman	jacket	shamrock	
cactus	locket	splendid	
campus	muffin	sunset	
cannot	napkin	talcum	
catnap	padlock	tickets	
comic	picnic	traffic	
fabric	pigpen	upset	
fantastic	plastic	velvet	
frogman	pockets		

TALCUM AND TWINS

Story Summary:

As the twins nap, Tam and her mom clean up around the house. Soon the twins get up. After the kids enjoy an afternoon snack, the twins begin their "terrible twos" trouble. First they overturn the rag-bag which Tam has just filled with tick-infested clothing. Then they go into their parents' room and play with their mom's talcum powder. They get it all over everything, including Tam's new black velvet jacket. Tam is upset and the twins have to sit in time-out chairs. Mom brushes and cleans the jacket until it is as good as new.

"Tam," said Mom, "put the twins' socks and caps in the ragbag on the deck. Ticks are on them."

As Tam put the things in the ragbag, the twins got up. Bill and Jill had a catnap. They ran to hug and kiss Mom and Tam.

"Mom, can I have a snack?" said Bill. "I want muffins and pop in a picnic basket."

"You can have a muffin, Bill," said Mom.

"Tam, get the snacks for the kids. Put them in the picnic basket. They can snack on the deck. Put the muffins on napkins."

"Yes, Mom," Tam said. As Tam got the snacks, Bill and Jill ran to the deck. They upset the ragbag. Socks, caps, frocks with rips and grit, and stuff that stank fell onto the deck.

"Quick, Tam, pick them up!" said Mom.
"You kids would get into pigpen slop if you could!" said Tam.

 Tam ran to the twins. Tam put the things back into the ragbag. The kids had the muffins. They put the napkins and cups back into the picnic basket.

As Tam put the napkins into the trash, the twins ran. They got into a big mess. Mom's talcum got on Tam's black velvet jacket.

 "The jacket! Bill and Jill, you are bad kids! I am mad and upset! Admit it. You flung that talcum onto my black velvet jacket."

The twins felt bad. Mom had to step in to fix the mess. Tam was still in a huff.

Mom said, "Twins, you have  upset Tam and you will have to sit. Do not get up until I tell you to."

 Tam said, "Mom, the jacket is such a mess. I cannot fix it. If I had a padlock, I would lock up the twins!"

"The twins are not big, Tam, and they did not want to mess up your jacket. I can fix it. I will brush it and hang it flat," Mom said.

Teacher/Parent Pages

Use the following questions to stimulate language growth, imagination, conceptual relationships, and higher-level thinking skills. These activities will encourage conversation and help develop language skills. Students must know that their ideas are important and that their questions will be heard. Have fun and accept all reasonable answers while praising and encouraging questioning from the students.

Vocabulary Expansion

Describe and define these words and phrases:

clean up	talcum powder	pigpen
agree	include	slop
terrible twos	padlock	bad luck
overturn	time-out chair	
tick	rescue	
infested	good as new	

Language Expansion Activities

1. Use the information from the story to create a puppet show.

2. Create a "Family Day" at school. Bring family members to school or show pictures of them and tell about the people in your family.

Language Expansion Questions

1. What was Tam doing at the beginning of the story?

2. When the twins woke up, what did they ask for?

3. Before their snack, what mischief did the twins get into?

4. What did the twins do after they ate their snack? Do you think they meant to ruin Tam's jacket?

5. How did Tam feel when she saw her brand new black velvet jacket covered with talcum powder?

6. The twins caused lots of trouble in this story. Have you or your brothers and sisters or friends ever caused any trouble? Write about it.

7. Tam was very angry with the twins at the end of the story. Have you ever been angry with someone who hurt you or ruined something of yours? What did you do?

8. In this story, Tam's mom made the twins sit on time-out chairs for creating such a mess. If your mother came in the room and found such a big mess, how do you think she would have reacted?

9. Do you think it's possible for all those things to happen to the children in such a short time?

10. Think of other things toddlers can do to make a mess.

AT THE CAMPUS

UNIT 15

Phonology/Syllabication Concepts

- Phoneme—syllable—word relationships:
    - A word must have at least one vowel phoneme.
    - A word has one or more **syllables**.
    - Each **syllable** contains **one vowel phoneme**.
    - A syllable that ends with a consonant phoneme is a **closed syllable**.

Vocabulary

admit	goblin	rabbit	*into*
basket	insect	ragbag	
Batman	jacket	shamrock	
cactus	locket	splendid	
campus	muffin	sunset	
cannot	napkin	talcum	
catnap	padlock	tickets	
comic	picnic	traffic	
fabric	pigpen	upset	
fantastic	plastic	velvet	
frogman	pockets		

AT THE
CAMPUS

Story Summary:

The day for the event at the campus has finally arrived. Tam looks lovely in her new black velvet jacket. She is very excited when her older cousin, Stan, finally arrives. Dad gives Tam a special present and takes the kids to the campus for the day's adventures. They see kids in costumes and meet the campus comic, Frogman Fred. After the show, Tam and Stan go to the campus snack shop. They have a fantastic time. Tam can't wait to tell her friend Pat.

"I have to admit, Tam," Dad said, "you are fantastic! That black velvet jacket is swell."

"Thanks to Mom," Tam said. "Mom did it. Mom is a doll."

"Is it ten yet?" Tam said. "I think I will have such fun. I want to get on with it."

"Tam, it is not ten yet, but I have a box for you," said Dad.

"Dad! A locket! Thanks!" Tam ran to hug and kiss him.

"And put this cash in your pocket," Dad said to Tam.

As Tam put the cash into her pocket, the bell rang. It was Stan.

The kids got into the van and Dad got them to the campus in a flash.

As they got out of the van, Stan ran into the campus comic, Frogman Fred.

Frogman Fred said, "You will have fun at the fantastic gig, but the campus snack shop is the hot spot. You will dig it. Got to run."

They left Fred and went on into the campus.

"Tam, I think I can spot Doc!" said Stan.

"What fun," said Tam, "I can spot kids in goblin, rabbit, shamrock, insect, and plastic cactus getups."

"This is swell, Stan," said Tam. "Have you got the tickets?"

"Yes," Stan said. "And on to the gig!"

When they got in, Tam said, "This is just fantastic. I think that is Frogman Fred!" Tam had a wink for the campus comic.  But Tam got red when Frogman Fred had a wink for Tam.

The kids could rap and jam with the cast. Frogman Fred was a ham!

 At the end, the kids set off to the campus snack shop. Tam sang with the kids and then Tam and Stan had clams in a basket.

"Thanks, Stan," Tam said. "I had much fun. But it is sunset, and Dad's van is at the snack shop."

They got into the van. "Dad, I have to tell you! We had fun at the campus! When I get back, I have to tell Pat the things Stan and I did! Frogman Fred! the campus snack shop! The kids' getups! Thanks, Dad. And thank you, Stan! I had fun!" Tam said.

———————

"Pat," Tam said. "I got to chat with Frogman Fred! It was a kick!"

"No!" said Pat. "Did the kids dress up?"

"Well, the kids did dress up," said Tam, "but...."

Teacher/Parent Pages

Use the following questions to stimulate language growth, imagination, conceptual relationships, and higher-level thinking skills. These activities will encourage conversation and help develop language skills. Students must know that their ideas are important and that their questions will be heard. Have fun and accept all reasonable answers while praising and encouraging questioning from the students.

Vocabulary Expansion

Describe and define these words and phrases:

getup	adventure	cash
arrive	costume	gig
lovely	campus snack shop	hot spot
excited	locket	tickets
present	gift	wink

Language Expansion Activities

1. Describe how you feel when you get to do something really special. Recall a special time and share it with your friends.

2. Several of the kids in the story were wearing costumes for the show. Ask your teacher if you can make a costume and create a story to go along with your costume.

Language Expansion Questions

1. Why was Tam so anxious? Can you remember an occasion that made you nervous? Write a story about it.

2. What did Dad think of Tam's new jacket? How do you know?

3. Try to remember all the different costumes the kids saw at the campus show. See if you can find the place in the story that tells about the costumes. Make a list of the costumes in the same order that they appeared in the story.

4. How do you think Tam felt about meeting Frogman Fred? Why?

5. The kids went to a snack shop after the show. Do you have a special cafe or restaurant where you like to go?

6. Choose one place in the story where you would like to go. Tell why.

7. Tam's father gave her a new locket and some money to put in her pocket. Has your father or any other adult ever given you anything special? Describe it.

8. At the end of the story, Tam and Pat were still talking. What things do you think they said? Act out the conversation with a friend.

9. On certain days of the year, people dress up in costumes. Do you have a favorite costume? Tell about it.

10. Suppose that Dad had a flat tire on the throughway and the kids did not get to see the show. Predict what might have happened. Explain how they might have felt.

THE SPRING PICNIC

UNIT 16

Phonology/Orthography Concepts

- Consonant clusters are consonant letter combinations representing **three different** consonant phonemes.
- Unit 16 consonant clusters are: **str**, **spr**, **spl**, **scr**

Vocabulary

Scott	street	*were*
scram	stress	
scraps	strict	
scrub	string	
split	strip	
splash	strong	
sprang	strum	
spring	sprung	
strap	strung	

THE SPRING PICNIC

Story Summary:

It's the end of the year, and Miss Pitt's class is planning to celebrate the end of its sixth grade year. Miss Pitt has too many things to do, so Dan volunteers to plan the picnic. Others help with the menu and with transportation. Plans are finalized for a wonderful spring picnic.

Miss Pitt had a wish that the class could have a big spring picnic. The kids were fantastic, and Miss Pitt was upset that they would finish the sixth grade.

"You were the best class. I think you should have a big picnic," Miss Pitt said to the kids. "But I must admit that I cannot plan it. Could you help?"

Dan sprang up and said, "Miss Pitt, I will plan the spring picnic for us. I can tell it's a lot of stress for you. You were strict, but you were the best, Miss Pitt."

"Mom can fix us a big ham," Dan went on, "and the kids said that they would help to fix the picnic lunch if I would get us a bus and plan the trip."

The bell rang. The kids met at the Tenth Street bus stop to discuss the picnic. "I think the moms will help us," Scott said to Dan.

When they got back to class, Miss Pitt said, "Dan, what are your plans?"

Dan said, "The bus will pick us up at six, at the Tenth Street bus stop. Traffic is not too bad then."

"Scott's mom and Sam's mom said they would help get us to the bus. They have big vans."

 "Sam, can you bring your bat and mitt?" . . . "Scott could strum and sing for us!" . . . "Bring Bob, Al!" . . . "Let's have a swim in the pond!". . . "Tam, could you bring Tab?" . . .

Sid thinks of tennis . . . Pat thinks of a brisk run at the track . . . Miss Pitt thinks of a long rest.

"Let's plan the things the class should bring," Dan said. Kim and Tam will bring chips and dips. Pat could bring pop. Mat will bring fish sticks. Kim could bring napkins.

"Put your things in strong plastic bags, class," Miss Pitt said.  "Then insects and bugs cannot get into them."

At last the bell rang. "We will have the best picnic in the land!"

Teacher/Parent Pages

Use the following questions to stimulate language growth, imagination, conceptual relationships, and higher-level thinking skills. These activities will encourage conversation and help develop language skills. Students must know that their ideas are important and that their questions will be heard. Have fun and accept all reasonable answers while praising and encouraging questioning from the students.

Vocabulary Expansion

Describe and define these words and phrases:

volunteer	fantastic	admit
menu	stress	plan
transportation	strict	bad traffic
finalize	promoted	plastic bags
wonderful	bus stop	insects

Language Expansion Activities

1. Plan an event for your class. You might write invitations, a menu, and a list of each person's responsibilities.

2. What is your favorite game or activity? Write directions for it. Be sure that the directions are in correct order.

Language Expansion Questions

1. Why does Dan volunteer to plan the spring picnic?

2. What kinds of things do the kids in the class think of doing at the picnic? What does Miss Pitt think of doing?

3. How were they going to get to the picnic?

4. Why do you think Miss Pitt warned the class to wrap all of their things in plastic bags?

5. What do you think Dan meant when he said that Miss Pitt was strict, but she was the best? Why is it important for teachers to be strict?

6. How do the other students feel about Miss Pitt? How does Miss Pitt feel about the class? What is said in the story that makes you think so?

7. Discuss the importance of carefully planning an event before it happens. What would have happened to the spring picnic if Dan had not made plans for it?

8. Write a story about a special event that you have had with your family or friends. Who made the plans? How did everyone know what needed to be done? Was anything important forgotten?

9. Discuss an event you would like to plan for your family and friends. How would you organize it? What things would need to be done in advance? Make a list of things to be done for the event.

10. Planning a special event is hard work, but it often doesn't seem like it. Why not? Why is some work less like work than play?

SCRAM!

UNIT 16

Phonology/Orthography Concepts

- Consonant clusters are consonant letter combinations representing **three different** consonant phonemes.
- Unit 16 consonant clusters are: **str**, **spr**, **spl**, **scr**

Vocabulary

Scott	street	*were*
scram	stress	
scraps	strict	
scrub	string	
split	strip	
splash	strong	
sprang	strum	
spring	sprung	
strap	strung	

SCRAM!

Book 2

Story Summary:

Pat, Nick, and Tam all have younger sisters and brothers in Mrs. Smith's first grade class. When the older kids discover that the first graders' picnic is scheduled for the same time and place as their own, they are outraged. They ride the bus to the picnic, and all sing songs while Scott plays his guitar. Miss Pitt gives them instructions about tickets, safety, and cleanup. When they arrive, the younger kids are already swimming in the pond. The older kids try to make them get out, and they are not very nice.

When Tam met the kids at the bus stop, she was upset. "Sis said that Mrs. Smith's class had plans to have a picnic, too!"

"Yes," said Nick, "Bud thinks they can have lunch with us."

"What?" said Pat. "They are just six. They cannot have a picnic with us! This is just splendid!"

"Well," Nick said, "the class might tell the brats to scram. They cannot have a picnic when this class has its picnic. They are just six."

Miss Pitt had six adults to help at the picnic. Jen Wells said, "The strap on this basket has split. Can I get some thick string from your class, Nell?"

"No problem, Jen," said Miss Pitt.

_____

When they got on the bus, Miss Pitt had a string of tickets for the kids. "Put your bus ticket in your pocket. You must have it to get back on the bus!"

"And when the picnic ends," Miss Pitt went on, "you must split up, pick up your scraps, and put them in trash cans."

At the picnic, Scott and the kids sang songs. Scott said he would strum as they sang, but then he sprang a string. "I will have to get this strung," Scott said.

"Let's jump in the pond and splash!" they said. Scott was strong; he could swim well. Al, Nick, Dan, Sid, Mat, and Sam ran to the pond with Scott.

 But Mrs. Smith's kids were in the pond. Sam said, "A hundred kids are in this pond. Miss Pitt's gang cannot swim with them!"

"This is just too much. You kids should scram!" Nick yells.

"Yes! You kids in Mrs. Smith's class have to scram!" they yell.

 "Let's get Tam and Pat," Scott said. "They will get Mrs. Smith's class to scram. Then the gang can jump in and swim!"

Which class will win?

Teacher/Parent Pages

Use the following questions to stimulate language growth, imagination, conceptual relationships, and higher-level thinking skills. These activities will encourage conversation and help develop language skills. Students must know that their ideas are important and that their questions will be heard. Have fun and accept all reasonable answers while praising and encouraging questioning from the students.

Vocabulary Expansion

Describe and define these words and phrases:

discover	selfish	pond
scheduled	rude	class spirit
outrage	strum	scraps
cleanup	force	guitar
arrive	tickets	spring a string

Language Expansion Activities

1. The end of the story reads: "Which class will win?" Write an ending for the story and tell what class eventually wins.

2. Make a poster that gives instructions for cleaning up an area after you have used it. Put it in the school cafeteria.

Language Expansion Questions

1. Explain why Tam, Nick, and Pat were upset.

2. What do you think Miss Pitt had in her picnic basket?

3. What did Miss Pitt tell the students to do with their bus tickets?

4. Miss Pitt gave instructions for the end of the picnic. What were they?

5. What songs do you think the kids sang while Scott played his guitar?

6. When all the boys raced to the pond to jump in, what did they find?

7. Why do you think the boys thought that they could not swim with Mrs. Smith's class?

8. Sometimes, older children reject younger children. Why do they do it? How does it make the younger children feel?

9. What does Pat really mean when she says, "This is just splendid"? Try to think of a time you might say the opposite of what you mean.

10. Why did Scott think that Tam and Pat could get Mrs. Smith's class to leave the pond? Why do you think the title of this story is *Scram!*?

A BIG SPLASH

UNIT 16

Phonology/Orthography Concepts

- Consonant clusters are consonant letter combinations representing **three different** consonant phonemes.
- Unit 16 consonant clusters are: **str**, **spr**, **spl**, **scr**

Vocabulary

Scott	street	*were*
scram	stress	
scraps	strict	
scrub	string	
split	strip	
splash	strong	
sprang	strum	
spring	sprung	
strap	strung	

A BIG SPLASH

Story Summary:

Pat and Tam, at their class's spring picnic, find their little sisters, Trish and Sis, swimming in the pond with all of the first graders from Mrs. Smith's class. They force all the younger children out so that their own friends can have the pond all to themselves. As the younger children get out, it begins to rain. Miss Pitt's sixth graders, undaunted, keep swimming. But the younger children carry out a plan of revenge.

Pat and Tam got Trish and Sis from the pond. Pat said, "You kids have to split. Miss Pitt's class is in the sixth. They  have to get in and swim. Run off, Trish."

Mrs. Smith's kids got up from the pond, and Miss Pitt's got in. Sis and Trish held hands.

 "You big kids just jump and yell and splash us!" Trish said, "You are bad!"

"Is Pat your big sis, Trish?" Sis said.

"Yes," said Trish, "and I will tell Dad what Pat and the big kids did to us."

Then Bud said to Nick, " You are big, but I am best."

"Just stop it Pat," said Trish. "You splash too much. You think you can splash us, but you will not win!"

Sis said, "If you stand still, they will go on and splash us. And I am too wet."

"But you are not wet just from the big splash," Trish said to Sis, "you got wet from up there."

Pat said, "If you kids are wet, put on a plastic bag. Then they will think that you are the trash!"

Trish and Sis ran off with Bud. At last they had a plan.

Bud got a big plastic bag from the bats and mitts. Trish got the plastic bag from Al's doll, Bob. Sis got the plastic bag that was on the big kids' lunch. Dick got his from Miss Pitt's picnic basket.

Mrs. Smith's kids put on the big black plastic bags. Miss Pitt's kids were still in the pond.

"I think I will have my picnic lunch on the bus. Then it will not get wet. Let's get to the bus, gang!" said Pat.

The kids ran to get their things, but they were wet. They did not have plastic bags on them.

"I cannot have this sog and slop for lunch!" said Pat. They were mad. They got back on the bus.

Lots of munchkins in black plastic bags were not wet.

"Did you have your spring picnic?" sang Mrs. Smith's munchkins. "You should have said it was your big splash!"

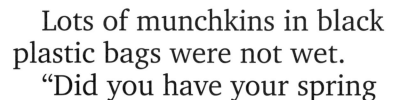

"I have to admit," Pat said, "Mrs. Smith's kids sprang a big trick on us."

Teacher/Parent Pages

Use the following questions to stimulate language growth, imagination, conceptual relationships, and higher-level thinking skills. These activities will encourage conversation and help develop language skills. Students must know that their ideas are important and that their questions will be heard. Have fun and accept all reasonable answers while praising and encouraging questioning from the students.

Vocabulary Expansion

Describe and define these words and phrases:

forced out	revenge	munchkins
all to themselves	split	trick
weather	sog and slop	force
undaunted	take advantage of	actually
carry out	sibling rivalry	cruel

Language Expansion Activities

1. Make a list of all of the kinds of weather possible. Then take turns describing each one.

2. Recall a time when you were small that older children took advantage of you. Describe the incident. Write a journal entry, explaining how it made you feel.

Language Expansion Questions

1. What did Pat and Tam do to get their little sisters' class out of the pond?

2. What did the sixth graders do to the first graders after forcing them out?

3. After the first graders got out, what started to happen?

4. When it started to rain, Trish said to Sis, "you got wet from up there!" What did she really mean?

5. Sometimes young children say things in funny ways. Think of some funny things that your younger brothers or sisters have said. Explain what they actually meant.

6. Pat said something cruel to her little sister, Trish. Why do you think she told Trish and her friends to "put on a plastic bag. Then they will think that you are the trash!"

7. Pat and Tam are actually very nice girls. Why do nice people sometimes do something that they are ashamed of later? Pat teased her little sister in front of all her classmates. How did Pat feel later?

8. Describe the plan that Bud, Trish, and Sis carried out with Dick and the other first graders.

9. Who were the munchkins? Why were the munchkins having so much fun?

10. Have you ever played a trick on anyone? Describe the event. Explain how you felt later.

PUMPKINS, MASKS, AND GOBLINS

UNIT 17

Phonology/Orthography Concepts

- Final blends are consonant letter combinations representing two **different** consonant phonemes at the end of a word.

- Unit 17 final blends are: **-st**, **-sk**, **-sp**, **-nt**, **-mp**, **-nd**, **-ld**, **-lk**, **-ft**, **-lp**, **-lt**, **-pt**, and **-ct**

Vocabulary

act	grasp	*two*
ask	kilt	*many*
best	last	*any*
blond	mask	
bold	mint	
clumps	pump	
dent	silk	
drift	soft	
dusk	stump	
frost	trick 'r treat	
grand	trust	

PUMPKINS, MASKS, AND GOBLINS

Story Summary:

The kids in Miss Pitt's class are anxiously awaiting Halloween. They talk to each other about what costumes they will wear and the great parade and party on Halloween. All but Nick, that is, who doesn't believe that he wants to wear a costume or go to the parade or to the party that follows. The pals are all wondering who will win the first place brass cup for best costume in the parade.

"The frost is on the pumpkin," Miss Pitt said to the class. "At dusk, when it gets black, a long string of kids in fantastic getups will trot up the path. At the end, men will hand a splendid brass cup to the kid in the best getup."

"Then the kids will yell, 'trick 'r treat' to moms and dads. Moms and dads will clap and sling bonbons, gum, nuts, and mints to the kids. Kids will have fun at sunset!"

"Soft bonbons with clumps of nuts would be grand," said Sam.

"Can I ask what you will dress as?" Miss Pitt said to Tam.

"Pat and I will dress up as traffic cops," said Tam. "The two of us will have cap guns, traffic pads and pens, and black hats with brass trim. At sunset, trust us to help stop the bad thugs!"

"And what are you thinking of dressing up as, Sid?" Miss Pitt said.

"I have a blond wig and a black dress that is silk with red velvet strings and trim. It is a kick! I will sing a smash hit song to you, Miss Pitt. You will dig the act!"

"Do tell, Sid! That's a fun getup. I wish you luck with the brass cup!" said Miss Pitt.

"And I ask you, Nick, what do you plan to dress up as?"

"I do not want to dress up, Miss Pitt. It's not as much fun as it was. I cannot get into it. I think I will get my sax and rest in bed."

Ring! Ring! The bell rang. It was the end of class. The kids split off in a flash to get set for fun at dusk. The plan was to get to the path when the dock clock rang six bells.

When six bells rang, the kids met. Six kids were goblins, a fat lad was a pink rabbit, and two kids had on frogman getups. As the kids would cross the path, they would pass moms and dads with baskets of things to toss to kids in masks.

The big man with the brass cup was at the last stop. The kids with the best getups got to sit on the stand.

The big man said, "The getups are grand! Two kids are dressed as pumpkins with black stumps and dents in their masks. A lad in a red kilt pumps bags that sing! This is grand!"

But the best was last. It was a kid in a fantastic frogman getup with a mask and a tank with a pump. The mask had black spots and bumps on it and the frogman had a limp.

"The brass cup will go to the frogman!" said the big man. "But, the kid must doff his mask!"

It was Nick! Kids in the stands said, "What a hit! Nick! The frogman was Nick!"

AT CAMP

UNIT 17

Phonology/Orthography Concepts

- Final blends are consonant letter combinations representing two **different** consonant phonemes at the end of a word.

- Unit 17 final blends are: **-st**, **-sk**, **-sp**, **-nt**, **-mp**, **-nd**, **-ld**, **-lk**, **-ft**, **-lp**, **-lt**, **-pt**, and **-ct**

Vocabulary

act	grasp	*two*
ask	kilt	*many*
best	last	*any*
blond	mask	
bold	mint	
clumps	pump	
dent	silk	
drift	soft	
dusk	stump	
frost	trick 'r treat	
grand	trust	

AT CAMP

Story Summary:

Pat, Tam, and Kim are headed for camp with the scouts. When they arrive, each girl is responsible for getting out supplies and setting up camp. As they take their sleeping bags out, they engage in horseplay, but Kim, who fails to listen to the counselor's instructions, gets hurt. She is upset, but after the counselors tend to her, she rejoins the group. Then it's time for dinner and a campfire with lots of skits and singing. The girls have a great time.

 Pat, Kim, and Tam were on the big red bus. They were off to Camp Shamrock to fish, sing, set up tents, swim, and picnic.

They had left at ten and would get to camp at six. It was a long way to camp.

Miss Moffit was the camp's boss and Miss Feld lent a helping hand.

The bus got them to camp at six. Pat said to Miss Moffit, "When I unpack, can Tam and I help set up the tents?"

"Yes," Miss Moffit said, "Miss Feld and I are glad to get the help! Kim, could you and Pat get the rest of the things off the bus?"

"I trust that you will not run with the bags, Kim. You could get cut," said Miss Moffit.

But as they got off the bus, Kim ran with the bags.

"Help!" Kim said with a gulp as she fell. "I just had to jump off and run." Kim had a split lip, and had two cuts on the left leg.

Miss Moffit and Miss Feld ran to help Kim. "Quick! Get the Red Cross Kit from the bus, Tam, and yell to Pat. I will put Kim on the grass and fix the cuts."

"I can get up and do my jobs," Kim said. "I just did not act as I should have, Miss Moffit."

Miss Moffit and Miss Feld did not yell at Kim. The two said that the bus still was not rid of the camping things and that the gals should hop to it.

When camp was set up Miss Moffit said, "Rub on this stuff, kids. Ticks and insects can sting you. If you get bit, just tell Miss Feld. You can get a bad red rash."

At six, the camp bell rang. It was the mess bell, and the kids could not get to the camp mess too fast.

But Tam said, "I think that is Pat!"

"Ants! Ants!" Pat was yelling. "I have a hundred red ants in my tent! Yuck! They can sting! Get them off this bunk!"

"Let's just brush them off your bunk and get to the camp mess," said Tam.

When they got into the mess, the gals had hot dogs on buns, chips, pop, and hot bran muffins.

"Yum! Yum!" said Pat. "I must admit, this is swell grub!"

At last, Miss Moffit said to the gals, "Miss Feld has lit the camp logs. What camp songs will you sing?" This was the best thing at camp.

"Let's sing a Rat Pack song, Miss Moffit," said Tam with a grin.

————————————

"You and Kim and Pat will have to sing that song," said

Miss Moffit. "Miss Feld, can you pick and strum a Rat Pack song?"

"Sing, gals! I will strum as you sing," said Miss Feld.

The gals did skits. They would sing and clap as they sang.

When they went back to the tent, Tam, Pat, and Kim did not get to bed until the clock said two!

They felt that Camp Shamrock was the best. It was such fun that they did not want it to stop.

Teacher/Parent Pages

Use the following questions to stimulate language growth, imagination, conceptual relationships, and higher-level thinking skills. These activities will encourage conversation and help develop language skills. Students must know that their ideas are important and that their questions will be heard. Have fun and accept all reasonable answers while praising and encouraging questioning from the students.

Vocabulary Expansion

Describe and define these words and phrases:

responsible	fail to listen	set up camp
sleep-away camp	counselors	campfire
supplies	memories	vow
mess hall	sleeping bag	skit
horseplay	inquire	

Language Expansion Activities

1. Pretend you are having a campfire. Sing, make up skits, and tell ghost stories.

2. Make a list of things you would need to take to a sleep-away camp.

Language Expansion Questions

1. Where were the girls going on the red bus?

2. What happened when the girls finally arrived at Camp Shamrock?

3. What happened to Kim when she failed to listen to Miss Moffit's instructions?

4. What creatures were all over Pat's bunk? How did Tam tell her to get rid of them?

5. Try to remember what the girls had for dinner. Look back in the story to help you remember.

6. After dinner, the counselors lit a campfire and the girls sang songs and told stories and performed skits. Have you ever sat near a campfire? Where were you?

7. Some kids like to go away to camp, but some kids do not. How do you feel about camp?

8. Kim was sorry that she didn't listen to Miss Moffit's instructions about carrying the bags. She got hurt because she did not listen. Have you or any of your friends ever been hurt because you didn't obey instructions? Write or tell your story.

9. A camp counselor has an important job. What do you think are some of his or her most important duties? Do you think you would like to be a camp counselor?

10. When the campfire was lit and the girls were singing songs, they vowed never to forget Camp Shamrock. Do you have any memories that you never want to forget? What are they?

THE
LANDFILL

UNIT 17

Phonology/Orthography Concepts

- Final blends are consonant letter combinations representing two **different** consonant phonemes at the end of a word.

- Unit 17 final blends are: **-st**, **-sk**, **-sp**, **-nt**, **-mp**, **-nd**, **-ld**, **-lk**, **-ft**, **-lp**, **-lt**, **-pt**, and **-ct**

Vocabulary

act	grasp	*two*
ask	kilt	*many*
best	last	*any*
blond	mask	
bold	mint	
clumps	pump	
dent	silk	
drift	soft	
dusk	stump	
frost	trick 'r treat	
grand	trust	

THE LANDFILL

Story Summary:

As a part of a project for school, the kids in Miss Pitt's class are collecting things to be taken to the landfill at the dump. They go to various homes and stores near their school and collect broken, unusable items that cannot be recycled. Sam's dad gets a pickup truck and is helping them with the project. A surprise is in store for them inside an old chest given to them by Ted.

"Lift that tank into the truck, Sam," said his dad. "Then get that tin desk. It is bent and its springs are split. I cannot mend it."

"Dad! You will have to help. I am not that strong," Sam said. "When the kids get to the truck, they can help you."

Nick, Sid, Al, and Mat ran to Sam's dad's big pickup truck to help. They got the bent, tin desk on the truck.

The kids got in the back of the truck and Sam's dad got to the next stop, Jen Wells's Pet Shop. "Have you got things to go to the landfill at the dump, Miss Wells?" said Sam.

"Yes, I do. This bent pump and this raft with a rip should go to the landfill. I have two bent pet bathtubs and a rabbit pen with rust that must go as well. Which of you will bring the bathtubs to the truck?"

"I will get them," said Nick. "Sam, you and Al go to Pam's Lunch Hut to get things for the landfill as I get the tubs into the truck."

"Pam," said Al, "do you have things for the landfill?"

"I'll check," said Pam. "I cannot mend that grill on the back steps. You can have it. This set of milk mugs can go as well as the two plastic plants and the bent clock."

"Thanks, Pam," said Sam and Al as they got the things to the truck.

"Next, let's get to Ted's Shell Shop. Ted has a bent-up chest that has to go to the landfill."

"Ted," said Mat, "do you still have that bent-up chest to go to the landfill?"

"Yes, I do, lads," Ted said. "But I will need help to bring it to the truck."

They ran to help Ted with the chest, and as they got it to the truck, the chest fell and split in two.

"WOW!" the lads said. "A map with an 'X.'"

"Well, lads!" said Ted. "I lost that map when I was on a big ship. The cash box was lost as well.

"You lads can have that map. I will help you to get to the 'X'! If the cash is still in the box, I will split it with you!"

Teacher/Parent Pages

Use the following questions to stimulate language growth, imagination, conceptual relationships, and higher-level thinking skills. These activities will encourage conversation and help develop language skills. Students must know that their ideas are important and that their questions will be heard. Have fun and accept all reasonable answers while praising and encouraging questioning from the students.

Vocabulary Expansion

Describe and define these words and phrases:

landfill	treasure map	sidetracked
project	"X"	cash in
collect	cash box	hidden
pickup truck	junk	adventure
dump	in store	old salt

Language Expansion Activities

1. Make a treasure map. Be sure to put an "X" on the spot where you plan to hide the treasure. Write directions to the spot.

2. Draw pictures of all the things the boys collected for the landfill. Print the name of each item under its picture.

Language Expansion Questions

1. What were the boys doing?

2. Who was helping the boys? Why did they need help?

3. Where did the boys go to collect broken, unusable items to take to the landfill at the dump? Why was everyone glad to have their help?

4. What items did the boys find at Jen Well's Pet Shop? Look back in the text to help you remember.

5. What was so special about Ted's old chest?

6. The boys were enthusiastic about collecting items for the landfill. Can you think of something in your house that you would have given them?

7. Where do your parents take broken things that nobody can use any more? Is there a landfill in your town? Why should we always try to recycle things that can actually be reused?

8. Do you think that the boys will find the treasure on the map?

9. Write a new ending for the story so that instead of a map, the boys really find a treasure in Ted's old chest. Would that ending be better? Why?

10. Ted is an old sailor. Some people call him an "old salt," because he has lived off the sea for many years. Would you like to be a sailor or go to sea for an adventure? Tell why. What might be a difficult part of a sailor's life? What would be the most exciting part?

A MATCH FOR CHICK

UNIT 18

Phonology/Orthography Concepts

- The phoneme /*ch*/ is encoded with the letters **-tch** after short vowels at the end of one-syllable words.

Vocabulary

batch	notch
catch	patch
clutch	pitch
ditch	sketch
fetch	stitch
hatch	stretch
hutch	switch
itching	watch
kitchen	
latch	
match	

A MATCH FOR CHICK

Story Summary:

One morning, Ted meets Chick as they are opening up at the dock. Chick tells Ted that he and Pam are going to get married, and he asks Ted to be his best man. When Ted sees Jen Wells arriving to open up her pet shop, they discuss the wedding and conclude that this is a good match. Ted recalls how Chick met Pam. Jen and Ted go inside and discover that her red hen's eggs are about to hatch into baby chicks.

Chick got a splendid catch of shrimp off a long ship at the dock. But when Chick got to his fish shack, the latch was stuck. Still, Chick had a big grin.

Ted said, "I think I can unstick your latch." Ted unstuck the latch and had to ask Chick, "Just what is that big grin of yours?"

"It was a big risk, but I felt I had to ask for Pam's hand. It's fantastic, Ted. Pam said yes! Will you act as best man at the wedding?" Chick said.

"Splendid!" said Ted. "I am glad to act as best man. And I am glad you two will wed. Anything I can do to help, just ask."

Then Ted had to get back to his shell shop.

He met Jen Wells at the pet shop. Ted said, "I have much to tell you!"

Jen was glad. "Chick and Pam are a fantastic match. Pam said they had a spat. I am glad they could patch things up."

"Yes," Ted said, "Chick thinks Pam is the best. Chick would not switch with any man. You and I can think of Chick and Pam as Mr. and Mrs.! Did I tell you how they met?"

"Last spring, Chick and Mat had to hitch up with a cab when  the gas pump on Chick's van went bad. The cab had to drop them off at Pam's Lunch Hut. Chick met Pam then," Ted said.

"The two struck it off. They had a long chat, and the next thing was, they were best pals. Chick said he felt Pam was his gal then," Ted said.

Jen undid the padlock on the pet shop, and the two of them went in.

"Do you think you could watch the red hen, Ted? The eggs should hatch into chicks. I have to catch them. I cannot let the cats get them!" Jen said.

"I will," Ted said. "But when you get them, that is the end of any chicks to catch at this dock!"

"Ted," said Jen, "you are just too much!"

Teacher/Parent Pages

Use the following questions to stimulate language growth, imagination, conceptual relationships, and higher-level thinking skills. These activities will encourage conversation and help develop language skills. Students must know that their ideas are important and that their questions will be heard. Have fun and accept all reasonable answers while praising and encouraging questioning from the students.

Vocabulary Expansion

Describe and define these words and phrases:

splendid catch of shrimp	hitch a ride
unstick a latch	truck stop
wedding	conclude
best man	struck it off
have a spat	hatching eggs
patch things up	chicks
ask for her hand	you're too much
a match for Chick	

Language Expansion Activities

1. Make a list of jobs that have to be done by Chick, Ted, Pam, and Jen when they open up their stores at the dock every morning.

2. Design an invitation for Chick and Pam's wedding.

Language Expansion Questions

1. Who was getting married?

2. How had they met?

3. What did their friends think about their marriage?

4. Why did Jen and Ted decide that this was a "fantastic match"?

5. How do you think Chick felt that morning? How do you think Mat will feel when he finds out?

6. The story says that Chick and Pam "had a spat," but they "patched things up." Explain what it means to "have a spat" with a friend.

7. Explain why Jen says, "Ted, you are just too much," at the end of the story. What do you think she means?

8. Chick, Jen, and Ted all went to their shops early in the morning to open up. List some reasons why people need to get to work early.

9. Ted was anxious to tell Jen the news about Pam and Chick. Can you explain why people enjoy spreading news to other people?

10. Discuss some ways that Mat's life might change when his dad and Pam are married. Are there any things that Mat might not like? What are some ways that Pam could help Mat?

THE
HATCHBACK

UNIT 18

Phonology/Orthography Concepts

- The phoneme /*ch*/ is encoded with the letters **-tch** after short vowels at the end of one-syllable words.

Vocabulary

batch	notch
catch	patch
clutch	pitch
ditch	sketch
fetch	stitch
hatch	stretch
hutch	switch
itching	watch
kitchen	
latch	
match	

THE
HATCHBACK

Story Summary:

Chick's old van can barely run any more. Chick is
working very hard, and now that his Fish Shack is
doing well, he can afford to replace it. He buys a
new red hatchback, and when he goes to Sam's
house to drop off some things for Mat, he surprises
Mat with the new family car. Mat thinks the van has
been stolen.

Chick said to the man filling his gas tank, "When you finish, could you check the clutch? It  sticks when I shift. Do you think you can fix it?" To himself, Chick said, "I wish I could get rid of this van."

"I have a splendid red hatchback to sell," the man said. "Do you want to test it? But watch it. You can run into lots of traffic on this strip. You do not  want to end up in a ditch."

When he got back, Chick said, "I would like to snatch up this hatchback as quick as I can. I will get rid of the van and have a slick red hatchback for the wedding trip."

Chick got the hatchback with cash and sped to Sam's.

Chick went into the kitchen to chat with Sam's mom. "Do I smell bran muffins?" he said.

"Yes. But you cannot have them. You are as bad as Sam and Mat! The muffins are for the wedding!"

The men were in the back, pitching a splendid tent for the fantastic  bash. They got Sam and Mat to help stretch the flaps and hitch the tent to a notch on a peg.

 "What do you think, Mat?" Chick said. Mat felt glad. At dusk, his dad and Pam would wed.

"As I was telling Sam," Mat said, "I think Dad and Pam are a grand match."

"It's not too long until six o'clock, Dad," Mat said. "I am just glad to get a stepmom. And Pam is the best."

"Chick," said Sam's dad, "if you would unlock your van, I could pack up your wedding gifts."

"And Mat and I could help!" said Sam.

"You can't put the gifts in the van," Chick said with a grin. "In fact, I don't have a van."

Mat got upset. "Dad, do you think a bandit could have snatched your van?" said Mat. "You will have to catch him!"

"Mat," Chick said with a grin, "you can stack the gifts in the back of this slick red hatchback!"

"This is swell, Dad! Let's get in and have a spin!"

Still, Mat had to admit to himself, "I wish I could have seen Dad catch a bandit!"

Teacher/Parent Pages

Use the following questions to stimulate language growth, imagination, conceptual relationships, and higher-level thinking skills. These activities will encourage conversation and help develop language skills. Students must know that their ideas are important and that their questions will be heard. Have fun and accept all reasonable answers while praising and encouraging questioning from the students.

Vocabulary Expansion

Describe and define these words and phrases:

hatchback	purchase	drop off
doing well	to bunk with	fantastic bash
afford	test drive	family car
get rid of	traffic jam	surprise
replace	snatch it up	bandit

Language Expansion Activities

1. Draw a picture of your ideal car. Then create a magazine advertisement that explains why people should choose this car instead of other ones.

2. Mat and Sam helped Sam's dad pitch a big tent for the wedding. Discuss what steps have to be taken to pitch a tent. Then write the directions in order.

Language Expansion Questions

1. What did Chick think about his old van?

2. Why was it important for Chick to test drive the hatchback?

3. What do you think made Chick decide to buy the hatchback?

4. Where was Mat going to stay while Pam and Chick were on their honeymoon?

5. What was Sam's mom doing to get ready for the wedding? Sam's dad? Mat and Sam?

6. Chick and Mat had a talk about Mat's feelings. Why was it so important for Mat to feel happy about the marriage?

7. People are usually eager to help prepare for special events like weddings and holidays. Discuss some things that your family does to prepare for special events.

8. Why did Mat think it would be exciting to watch his dad catch a bandit?

9. What people specialize in catching criminals? Can you explain why the work of police officers is so dangerous?

10. Many kids have one parent, a mom or a dad. What kinds of things might those kids worry about if their parent plans to get married?

FANTASTIC BASH AT SUNSET

UNIT 18

Phonology/Orthography Concepts

- The phoneme /ch/ is encoded with the letters **-tch** after short vowels at the end of one-syllable words.

Vocabulary

batch	notch
catch	patch
clutch	pitch
ditch	sketch
fetch	stitch
hatch	stretch
hutch	switch
itching	watch
kitchen	
latch	
match	

FANTASTIC BASH AT SUNSET

Story Summary:

Sam's parents are hosting Pam and Chick's wedding. Mat and Sam help to erect a huge tent in the backyard. Later, they pester Sam's mom, who is preparing the food. Pam gets Sam's mom to help her list all of the wedding gifts so she can write thank-you notes. Many friends attend the wedding, and at sunset Pam and Chick leave for their honeymoon.

Sam's mom and dad said they would have a fantastic bash. The wedding would be at sunset. They had many jobs to finish, but it was fun.

"The tent is up," Sam said to his mom. "Can Mat and I have a snack?"

"You two can snitch just one sandwich. But if you gulp all the clam dip, I will not have any left for the wedding! I am watching you!" Sam's mom said, "I have to chill this punch. And I still have to help Pam."

Sam's mom said to Pam, "What can I do to help you?" "You could print a list of the splendid gifts that Chick and I got. I will get a pen, a pad, and stamps. I must send a thank-you for the gifts."

They got many gifts: a set of matching glass goblets from Miss Pitt; a black chest with shells on top from Ted; six linen napkins from Jen; a kitchen hutch from Sam's mom and dad; and a brass ship's clock from the men at the dock.

Sid's gift was a pen-and-ink sketch of the dock.

Al would bring lots of film and flash bulbs and get snapshots for the wedding album.

Pat, Tam, and Kim said they would help Sam's mom.

When it was six o'clock, Chick said, "Let's get on with this wedding!"

Ted, the best man, held the wedding rings. Pam had a dress of soft pink silk. Chick's black tux had a crisp press.

 When the man of the cloth said to Pam, "Will you have this man?" Pam said, "I will."

Next, Chick said, "I do." A kiss was next, and the two were Mr. and Mrs.

———

Then, many pals had to rush up to wish Pam and Chick well.

Sam's mom had lots of snacks and drinks in the kitchen and on the deck. And Mat and Sam could snitch as much as they could stuff in!

A blond gal sang with the band. The kids from Mat's class sang, too. Sam's dad  said they sang off-pitch, but Miss Pitt said they had talent.

"Um," Sam's dad said, "that is talent?"

 At last, the sun was setting on the fantastic bash. Pam and Chick had a hug and a kiss for Mat. Then Chick swept Pam up and put her in the red hatchback. They would have a quick exit.

Nick, Dan, Sam, and Mat had said they would wax Chick's hatchback as a gift. The wax job was splendid. But the pals had strung red and pink strips and tin cans to the back. The glass said, "Just Wed."

Teacher/Parent Pages

Use the following questions to stimulate language growth, imagination, conceptual relationships, and higher-level thinking skills. These activities will encourage conversation and help develop language skills. Students must know that their ideas are important and that their questions will be heard. Have fun and accept all reasonable answers while praising and encouraging questioning from the students.

Vocabulary Expansion

Describe and define these words and phrases:

erect	wedding ring	pen-and-ink
thank-you note	wedding album	sketch
snapshot	sing off-pitch	a crisp press
host	have talent	ceremony
pester	kitchen hutch	reception

Language Expansion Activities

1. The story tells about some special gifts the kids had given. These gifts did not cost money. Make a list of some gifts you can give to the people you love—without spending money.

2. Create a special menu for refreshments at a wedding reception.

Language Expansion Questions

1. Sam's mom and dad were the hosts for the wedding. What are a host's responsibilities?

2. When Mat and Sam went into the kitchen to try to get some of the wedding refreshments, Sam's mom would only let them have one sandwich. Later, at the reception, they could have as much as they wanted. Can you explain why?

3. What gifts did Pam and Chick get? What other things do they need?

4. Sam's mom helped Pam list the gifts so she and Chick could write thank-you notes. Why is it so important to write a thank-you note when you receive a gift?

5. Pam was going to be Mat's stepmom. The story didn't tell what happened to Mat's real mom. What do you think could have happened?

6. When people live together, they have to be considerate of other people. What changes might Chick and Mat have to make when Pam comes to live with them?

7. Why do people get dressed up and try to look their best for special occasions like weddings? Have you ever seen anyone in a tux?

8. Miss Pitt said that the kids in her class "had talent." Sam's dad said, "That is talent?" What do you think he meant?

9. What special talent do you have? Write about it.

10. Everyone has talent, but there are particular things that are difficult for every person. What things are difficult for you?